For the Joh... ...d
Brister Library —

Here is yet another
book for the
Special Collection

William C. Statt

Oct 21, 1976

SURGEON, TRADER, INDIAN CHIEF

Henry Woodward of Carolina

BY WILLIAM O. STEELE

Illustrated by Hoyt Simmons

sandlapper press, inc.

SURGEON, TRADER, INDIAN CHIEF

Library of Congress Catalog Card Number: 72-76381

FIRST EDITION
Copyright © 1972 by Sandlapper Press, Inc.

International Standard Book Number: 0-87844-008-9

Published by Sandlapper Press, Inc.
P.O. Box 1668, Columbia, S.C. 29202
Manufactured in the United States of America

For Sue Steele
of Middle Tennessee

BOOKS BY WILLIAM O. STEELE

Historical Fiction

The Buffalo Knife / Wilderness Journey / Winter Danger /
Tomahawks and Trouble / The Lone Hunt / Flaming Arrows /
The Perilous Road / We Were There on the Oregon Trail /
The Fair Fronter / We Were There with the Pony Express /
Trail Through Danger / Wayah of the Real People /
Tomahawk Border / Wilderness Tattoo

Tall Tales

Davy Crokett's Earthquake / Daniel Boone's Echo /
Andy Jackson's Water Well / The Spooky Thing /
The No-Name Man of the Mountain

History

Westward Adventure: The True Stories of Six Pioneers /
The Old Wilderness Road: An American Journey

Biography

Francis Marion: Young Swamp Fox /
The Story of Daniel Boone / The Story of Leif Ericson

CONTENTS

7

Alone in a Strange Land

The Englishman stood on the hot sands of a Carolina beach, surrounded by the naked Cusabo. It was July 1666, and his ten-month visit with the Indians had begun.

Across the bay the ship with his departing countrymen rocked at anchor. The sails were raised and at once filled by the quickening wind. The anchor chain rattled up out of the water. The ship turned slowly around and headed for the Atlantic Ocean.

Dr. Henry Woodward snatched his floppy black hat from his head and waved it in the air. From the poop deck of the ship Lieutenant Colonel Robert Sandford, the leader of the exploring party, returned Woodward's farewell with his hand. The Indian boy

in breechclout beside Sandford waved also. The boy was the nephew of the chieftain of the Cusabo. He was a hostage in a way, and his safe treatment among the British should make Henry Woodward's stay among the Carolina natives safe too.

Woodward, the surgeon on board ship for this British voyage of exploration, had volunteered to stay and learn the Indians' customs and language. Colonel Sandford had been delighted to accept his offer. He had promised to return for Woodward in ten months, bringing the chief's nephew back to the Cusabo.

Ten months was too short a time in which to try to understand Indian ways, but a start had to be made somewhere if the British hoped to settle here and survive. The Lords Proprietors of Carolina greatly desired a settlement. Woodward was willing to do his part in the enterprise by living with the Cusabo and learning all he could. Besides, he was full of curiosity about these people and eager to know more about their ways.

Woodward placed his hat back on his head and pulled the brim low over his forehead. The glare from the sand and sea was painful to his eyes. Overhead, gulls wheeled and screamed. A line of pelicans flapped their awkward way between Woodward and the ship, but Henry did not see them. He only saw the ship as it grew smaller and smaller.

The Cusabo stirred restlessly about the beach. They had work to do, but they were too polite to leave. Still Woodward watched the boat on the far line of the bay. He didn't yearn to be on board, nor did he regret his choice to remain behind. He just wanted to watch the vessel disappear, the last familiar thing in a strange world.

The chieftain beside him understood. He squeezed Henry's arm encouragingly from time to time. The chief's young wife stood on the other side of the white man. She too waited, still and patient as her husband.

The gnats and flies were fierce. Woodward could not stand still for slapping at them, but the insects did not seem to bother the Indians. Their faces and bare bodies were greased with bear oil to discourage bites.

Later today Woodward would grease himself as the natives did. In time too he might venture to put aside his trousers and shirt and wear only a breech-clout like the Cusabo. Certainly he wanted the Indians' comfortable moccasins. His British boots were too hot and heavy for this almost tropical country.

At last the ship was gone from sight. Only porpoises could be seen in the bay, leaping in graceful curves. Only seabirds diving for fish filled the distant blue horizon.

The chief placed his hands on Woodward's shoulders and turned him away from the bay, toward the huts nestling in cool shade under the pine trees. Beyond the town were orchards and fields of green, waving corn. Woodward smiled at the quiet beauty of his new home. It would be an ideal place to live—if all went well between him and the Indians.

He glanced around at the smiling faces. Were the villagers really glad to have him among them? With Indians who could tell? Their faces seldom betrayed their true feelings. Smile they might with friendliness, even while they seethed inside with hatred of him for intruding into their lives.

Certainly these people had seemed happy to

have him among them a few hours earlier in the town house. Then the chief had taken Woodward by the hand and led him to a raised platform, where there was a seat wide enough to hold half a dozen men. This was the throne. The chief sat with his wife on his right side and the doctor on his left. Sitting there above the British and Indian spectators, Woodward had been welcomed to the town of Orista. With a brief ceremony the chieftain had adopted him into the Cusabo tribe.

Then the villagers had shouted and cheered and danced about in great joy. The noise had been terrific, and Woodward had been startled that all of it was for him. However, Colonel Sandford and the chieftain had been pleased at the demonstration. It was a fine beginning to a hopeful future—a future of friendly relations between the Cusabo of Carolina and the British newcomers.

Now that his friends had gone, the dangers which lay ahead suddenly hit Henry Woodward with full force. His survival depended on so many things. What if Sandford returned without the chief's nephew? Would he be killed in retaliation? What if

Sandford never returned? What of Woodward's future then? What if he broke a religious custom and the Cusabo became angry at him and demanded his death? Who would save him then? What if he and the whole village were captured by raiding Indians and taken away to some distant land to be slaves?

What if? . . . What if? . . .

He snorted contemptuously. He wouldn't let his fears get the better of him. Life was always a gamble; it was always filled with peril in both familiar places and strange surroundings. As a British surgeon he knew how suddenly disaster could strike, and how little good it did to worry about what lay ahead. He had never been one to fret over unseen dangers. Why should he begin here and now in Carolina?

Suddenly he threw back his head and laughed at his foolishness. This was an adventure! He was lucky to be here. He picked up his possessions—an iron pot, a coat, an axe and a dagger, a leather bag of surgical instruments—and walked with a light heart toward the town, surrounded by the Cusabo. Let come what would!

The Tenant of Carolina

For a young surgeon with no home and few possessions, July 8, 1666, had been quite a day. Besides being adopted by the Cusabo tribe, Woodward had been given formal possession of Carolina by Robert Sandford, who was secretary of the Lords Proprietors of Carolina. He had made Woodward "Tenant at Will" to hold the province for them, and now a whole great area of the rich and marvelous New World belonged to Henry Woodward.

Carolina stretched from the colony of Virginia

16

southward to Spanish Florida, and from the Atlantic westward to the Pacific Ocean. This vast territory had been granted by King Charles of England to a group of lords who were his friends. These Lords Proprietors wanted colonists, who would have to pay rents and provide revenue.

On the island of Barbados in the West Indies there had been much unpleasant strife and rivalry between various political parties. Henry Woodward and other English settlers there had lived in a constant state of anxiety. As more and more newcomers crowded into the island, the discontented Englishmen decided to leave. But where could they go?

There was unoccupied land along the Carolina coast of the American mainland; it was suitable for farming and stock raising. The Lords Proprietors wanted people there. So those who were dissatisfied with conditions in Barbados had left and begun a settlement in the area around Cape Fear, in what is now North Carolina.

This region had been a disappointment to the

17

Barbadians, however. There had been trouble with the Indians and a massacre was feared. Many had decided it would be best to seek another place to live. Taking a ship hired by the Proprietors with a small crew, Robert Sandford had sailed southward from Cape Fear to explore. They had found several excellent sites for colonizing, but the area around Port Royal Bay pleased the explorers most.

Here was fertile soil, good timber, fine harbors and a network of creeks. More than that, the Cusabo Indians of Orista were friendly and begged the British to settle in their territory. This was welcome news to men desiring to get on with the daily tasks of settlement without the disturbing fears of an Indian uprising. The Englishmen had hurried back to Cape Fear to report on the success of their voyage.

To bind their friendship with the Cusabo, called by the British the Port Royal Indians, Sandford had agreed to take the chief's nephew away with him so that the boy might learn British ways and speech. In return he had asked the chief to let one of his followers live at Orista until he came back. The chief had been delighted at the idea and accepted twenty-year-old Henry Woodward, who had volunteered to stay until Sandford returned in ten months.

Who was this volunteer—this Henry Woodward?

He was an obscure resident of Barbados who came to the Cape Fear settlement as a surgeon. His place of birth is uncertain, but the date is reckoned as *about* 1646. Nothing is known of his early schooling, or whether he went to medical school.

In former times the barber's craft was a profession united with that of surgeons. It may be that Woodward was merely a barber, proficient in the minor operations of blood-letting and the drawing of teeth, as well as in the further business of shaving, trimming beards and dressing hair.

Robert Sandford, a most proper person, referred to him as a "chirurgeon," one whose profession it was to heal by operating with the hand. Today's word *surgeon* is derived from that early form. In all likelihood Woodward was a bona fide surgeon with instruments and medicines in a black bag, the usual mark of one of his calling.

Actually, it mattered not about Woodward's past and what his status was. What mattered was what

19

he could do in this new-found land of America. The raw wilderness had ways to prove a newcomer's worth and decide his future.

But what possible future could a youth have, living among red natives, learning to jabber in their tongue and shoot a bow and arrow, feasting and dancing with them the whole night long? What possible good could come of Woodward becoming a white Indian?

Who knows what the surgeon thought? But in the summer of 1666, at the Cusabo village of Orista on what is now Parris Island, he was at the edge of vast unknown regions stretching westward, a New World. And he owned it. Almost anything might happen in such a place. Surely he looked forward with excitement to whatever the future held.

A Bowl of Stew

The Orista chieftain had wasted no time settling the Englishman into village life. As soon as Henry was taken into the tribe, the chief showed him a corn field which was to be his, as well as an open-sided hut. He then commanded his niece, Pala, to take care of the corn and the garden and to prepare the doctor's food and mend his clothes.

It was Pala's brother who had sailed away with Sandford. Henry hoped the Englishman was as generous and kind in caring for the boy as the Cusabo chief was to him.

21

Pala tanned a strip of deerhide until it was as soft as English velvet. This was a breechclout for Henry to wear in place of his breeches. The breechclout was passed between one's thighs and over a belt so that the ends of the flap hung loose in front and behind.

Henry felt terribly naked and exposed in it, but in time he became used to wearing so little. What was worse was his awful white skin. Never had he been so conscious of its sickly color as here among these dark-skinned natives. He was too embarrassed to walk about the town until his skin was browner. But every morning Pala rubbed bear oil on him and he sunned himself. Soon he was as tan as any villager.

Of his old clothes he kept only his floppy hat to wear, for he never got used to the bright glare and found the hat's brim a help to his weak eyes. Hat, breechclout and moccasins were his daily outfit.

Pala wore even less than he did. Some days she dressed in only a short deerskin skirt. Other times she made an apron of the long grey moss which grew in the trees. Everyone wore as little as possible during the sultry days of summer.

From the very first day Pala began teaching Woodward the Cusabo language. At each meal she told him the words for his food. He could eat none of it till he pronounced the words to Pala's satisfaction. While he ate, she made him repeat the words over and over.

It was a fine way to learn the tongue, and Woodward was quite pleased with his progress as the summer passed. He tried to teach Pala only two words—his name. The best she could do was "Heeen—reee Woooo—arrrddd."

One day he returned from exploring the island to find a pot of venison stew simmering over the hot ashes. Pala was in the garden gathering watermelons, so he picked up a large wooden spoon and began to ladle the stew into a clay bowl. Pala came flying up and stopped him.

"What is that?" she asked, pointing to the stew.

Henry opened his mouth to answer, but he could not think of the words for stewed deer meat. He shook his head and went back to helping himself to the stew.

Pala snatched the spoon from his hand. Then she

23

poured his half-filled bowl back into the pot. "No food, Heen-reee, till you remember the words," she scolded.

He flopped down on a wooden stool and went over all the words he could think of. But for all his hunger he could not recall anything for venison stew, even though he had eaten it often with Pala. He fumed and fussed and grew hungrier and hungrier. At last he gave up and begged Pala to tell him the words and let him eat.

Pala shook her head. "No," she replied. "You will stay hungry."

"I will go and see my neighbors," he told her. The Cusabo were courteous and offered food to whoever came to call.

He moved off, but she grabbed the hat from his head and said, "I will cut it to pieces, if you go!"

Henry was startled. He didn't know whether she was serious or not. He had found her very determined and stubborn at times. She knew that he would miss his hat. He thought a moment. He had best not let her bully him this time, else he might be doomed to future domination. He decided to go on and take a chance that she was too kindhearted to destroy something he valued so much.

Once again he walked away. This time Pala grabbed the leather thong which held up his breechclout. "I will cut away your breechflap," she said viciously, waving a knife before him, "and you will be ashamed to visit your neighbors."

Henry stopped. That was certainly true. He was still rather shy about the scantiness of clothes among the Cusabo. It was his upbringing as an English gentleman, he supposed. Nakedness didn't bother the villagers at all. They would pay no attention if he walked into their huts stark naked. But Pala knew that without his flap he would be embarrassed. She had outsmarted him this time.

He sat back down on the stool. This was undoubtedly a most ridiculous situation. Here he was, thwarted by a mere slip of a girl and unable to eat because of her obstinacy. Who would have thought this could happen to a British surgeon who was holding the Province of Carolina for the mighty Lords Proprietors of England?

Suddenly he began to chuckle. Then great peals

of laughter roared forth. He rolled to the ground and lay there shaking with laughter till his sides ached.

Pala watched him. Finally she could not resist joining in. The two of them sat guffawing and giggling till the nearby villagers came running to see what was happening.

"This wildcat of a girl," Woodward called out in English to nobody, for no one could understand what he was talking about, "is starving me because I can't remember the words for venison stew."

"I am very mean," giggled Pala to her watchers, and even Henry could understand what she said.

She and Woodward burst out in fresh laughter. The villagers smiled to each other and said that the spirit folks must have stolen their wits to make them act so silly. But they were pleased that the Englishman found life at Orista so pleasant and jolly. They drifted away to their huts.

All at once the words Henry wanted came rushing to his tongue. He turned and shouted them at Pala and she clapped her hands elatedly. She came up to him and rubbed his shoulders with the palms of her hands, noisily sucking in her breath all the while. This was the Cusabo way to denote friendship.

"You eat now," she smiled. "Eat all of the stew."

All was forgiven. Woodward gave her braided hair a hard yank. "But you are *mean,*" he teased in his awkward Indian speech. "I will get the conjurer to cause you to break out with horrible sores."

At once Pala's face became serious. "You must not say such things, Heeen-reee," she told him, looking around. "It can happen. Conjurers are very powerful."

It was true, and Woodward knew he shouldn't have mentioned such a threat. There were many different kinds of conjurers; they had enormous power and the Cusabo feared them. One conjurer might put a spell on someone—weaken the muscles in his arms and legs so that they were useless—or cause other illnesses. Another might cure diseases with herbs and roots. Anyone who wanted to harm anyone else might have a conjurer send rattlesnakes to bite the victim.

Woodward hung his head and looked remorseful. "I was so hungry my brains weren't working properly. I'm sorry, Pala," he said.

Pala handed him the bowl of stew. "Eat, and even if you forget the word for stew, do not ever forget to be respectful of the conjurers."

Who is the Savage?

The hurricane season passed with no damage to Orista. A few times strong winds swept across the island and town, carrying away the gnats and mosquitoes and leaving behind tingling cool air. Woodward was delighted, for he had had enough of insects and summer heat.

Now autumn was upon them and Henry looked forward to traveling inland with the villagers to gather the ripe nuts. Sometimes only a few men and women went; more often, however, it was a large family group. Several times Henry was asked to join these expeditions. They would be gone for weeks, paddling up the inland network of streams till the hardwood forests were reached. Then they would beach their dugout boats and roam the woods, camping wherever night found them. There was much joking and teasing while the cane baskets and deerskin sacks were filled, and also while they rested around the campfires at night.

Nut-gathering could hardly be described as hard labor. It was more like a pleasant holiday outing, and Henry enjoyed himself immensely. He was amazed at the abundance of nuts, and at how little effort it took for the Indians to fill dugout after dugout with hickory nuts and walnuts, acorns and chestnuts.

Back in Orista the hickory nuts were pounded in a hollow stone mortar with a long, flat-bottomed pestle of stone. When the nuts were ground fine, they were dumped into a pot of boiling water. This was strained and what was left was a thick whitish oil which was sweet and rich. This was called hickory milk. It was used with hot bread and Henry preferred it to the dairy butter he had been accustomed to all his life.

The walnuts were also pounded in a mortar and the oil used by the Cusabo to grease their hair. Pala used the walnut hulls to make an olive-colored dye with which she stained her reed baskets. Acorns from many different oaks were boiled to rid them of their bitterness, then crunched as tidbits, or the nuts were pounded into a fine flour and used to make bread.

Some days Pala and the doctor would make short journeys into the woods on the mainland for persimmons. She made a bread from the pulp of this fruit by pressing it through a sieve to get rid of the skin and seeds. They also brought back from these jaunts grapes and haw berries and little sour crab-apples.

The Cusabo believed in hearty eating. They ate any time they were hungry, night or day. They also believed in sharing their food, and not a day passed that some villager didn't drop by Henry's hut to leave freshly baked bread, melons and vegetables from their gardens, or turkeys and ducks and haunches of venison.

Henry led a lazy, happy life. He could now talk easily with Pala and often spent the day chatting with her as she wove cane mats to hang on the open sides of his dwelling, or as she pounded corn for the next meal's bread. If Pala was away fishing or visiting her kin, the doctor was content to sit with his back against a pine and watch the white clouds fluff up from the horizon and go skimming across the bright indigo sky.

He was fascinated by the great variety of bird life on the island and its beaches. On Barbados he had never paid much attention to such things. Now he roamed about, watching the longlegged birds on the mud flats and the small sandpipers trotting along just out of reach of the lapping waves.

How many times he wished for a spyglass to watch the fish-hunting ospreys hanging motionless above the bay. And he always liked to see the crazy little green parrakeets, who delighted in preening their bright feathers on the roof of his hut, or squawking wildly about him in the trees and bushes.

It was a lovely island. Never had he been so easy in mind and at peace with the world as here at Orista among his new friends, the Cusabo. His companions on board ship had thought him a bit mad to volunteer to live with the Indians. They believed the Carolina savages were little more than wild animals, living in filth and wracked with diseases. More than one of his fellow Englishmen had told him he would never get enough to eat, for it was well known that Indians, lazy and disgusting in their habits, starved the year round.

"Ha!" exclaimed Henry, as he reached into a basket and lifted out a handful of muscadine grapes. "They should see me now, stuffing myself every day with every kind of dainty." He glanced over to where oysters and a flounder lay in wet moss, waiting for Pala's attention, and groaned happily.

"The King of England himself," he said, "leads no grander life than I."

He spit out grape seeds. It was wonderful to be a young man living in a land of plenty, among kind and considerate people. Why had he once thought the natives might treat him cruelly?

Even the conjurers, who were touchy and standoffish when it pleased them to be so, treated him with friendliness, even with respect. It might be that they considered him one of them, since they were curious about the instruments and the vials of medicine in his surgeon's bag.

The Cusabo had few possessions they valued. A person could walk into any dwelling and inspect and handle any object inside and it was not considered rude. Often the conjurers would visit him; without a word they would sit on the hut floor and open his black bag. How they marveled at the sharp scalpel that folded up like a pocket knife, the forceps, the probes, the scissors and the ligatures of double silk thread. They would ask questions about these and listen intently to what Woodward told them. They were interested in everything except the amputation saw. This they pronounced evil.

Woodward never understood why this was so until one autumn day when he was collecting shells along the beach. The wind was chilly, and he had on his British coat. Suddenly he spied a dugout coming through the waves at great speed. Those in it were paddling furiously.

When the dugout reached the shore, Henry

waded into the sea to help beach it. In the bottom of the boat lay a small boy, his leg and foot a mangled mass of bloody flesh and jagged, splintered bones.

The surgeon whipped off his coat and placed the boy in it so that his leg would be steady when he was carried. Then he scooped him up and hastened with the family toward their dwelling. Placing the boy on a bed, he rushed off for his surgical instruments.

When he returned with his black bag, a conjurer was there boiling herbs and mixing powders and ungents. He glared hostilely at the Englishman. Henry knew he was unwanted, but he ignored the conjurer's enmity and explained that he wanted to saw the boy's leg off. In its present condition the crushed leg was bound to become worse and then gangrene would set in and kill the child. Unless the leg were cut off, the boy would not live.

"Take his leg away from the rest of him!" exclaimed the conjurer in shocked tones. "The Cusabo are not such savages as to deform a person. To cut off his leg would humiliate him so that he could never again show himself to others."

The conjurer sneered at Woodward in disgust.

"You white conjurers know nothing of decency. Leave with your evil sawing tool! Leave!"

Woodward left. What a topsy-turvy world the conjurer had shown him! The British thought the red natives were barbarians for their crude ways and customs, while at the same time the Indians were sure that was true of the whites. Strange.

But the Cusabo had never forced their ways upon him, and he certainly had no intention of pressing his on them. He hurried home with the conjurer's chants sounding shrill and wild above the wind behind him.

Shadows and Silence

The Orista town house was a large, round building with a thatched roof of palmetto leaves and side walls of cane, plastered over with lime made from ground shells. The chief and his advisers met here to attend to official affairs and to hold councils with the whole village. This was where Henry Woodward had been accepted by the Cusabo and adopted into the tribe. Here also visitors were received and dances performed.

In the center of the floor was a raised clay

hearth where a fire burned the year round. Certain old women tended this sacred fire, which was a part of all their ceremonies, though Woodward never noticed any person worshipping it or performing any religious ceremonies to it as they did to the sun and the moon.

During the winter months the villagers often went to the town house simply to be together. Pala liked going there to gossip and sew with the other women. Henry went with her. He enjoyed watching the gambling games, or listening to stories of tribal history or great hunts and battles of long ago.

Here one bitter winter night he heard for the first time of scaly men who in times past had lived in Carolina. These men had tails several feet long, thick as a man's arm and as hard as bone. Their tails were not movable, and when one of them sat down a bench with an open bottom was necessary for his tail to fit in. If they sat on the ground, unless holes were dug to accomodate their stiff, scaly tails, these men couldn't rest.

Once a conjurer told him how to make a child

into a giant. When the child was very young, certain herbs were rubbed on its body until the bone became soft as wax. Then the child was bent and stretched, bent and stretched, until its size was slowly increased.

Woodward was entertained by all these tales. He had never heard such lies in his life, although the tales were always told as solemn truth.

The cold weather passed swiftly and spring came. The island meadows were filled with new grass and sweet-smelling flowers. Migrating flocks of birds filled the skies all day, and mating alligators bellowed the night long from their swamp holes.

The Cusabo welcomed the new planting season with many religious ceremonies to the sun and with blessings of fields by the priests. There were feasts and dances, and at times the drinking of a black bitter tea made from yaupon leaves which purged the drinker and made him healthy.

Spring was the time to repair fish nets and to build fish traps in the tidal creeks. Arrows were made for hunting and bowstrings were renewed. Clay was brought from inland sources and some of the women made new water pots and flat shallow pans in which sea water sat till it evaporated, leaving much-needed salt in the bottom of the pans.

Wooden vessels were carved and dwelling roofs replaced. Every villager was busy from morning till night. Even the smallest of children were sent out to gather grasses and reeds and canes for household uses.

Henry watched these activities with interest. Pala hardly spoke to him, she was so occupied with her many tasks. It seemed to the doctor that he was in the way, and this time he had to himself would be excellent for journeying about the inlets and creeks and mud flats in Pala's dugout. He must know the lay of the surrounding area before Sandford and the British colonists returned to settle here. That way he could act as their guide and be in everyone's good graces. Certainly the Lords Proprietors would be pleased with him and advance him in station—perhaps offer him a piece of land for his help.

One afternoon Henry paddled to an island not too far up a river from Orista. He had been gone all day and he was tired. But he had seen a path leading from the island's beach inland, and he was curious.

He beached his craft and followed the path through the woods. Bushes pressed in on him and briar and grape vines entangled him, but he pushed on. Overhead the trees were laced together and the light grew dimmer and dimmer.

At last he reached a building, well made of wood and canes covered with a thick plaster of ground shells and water. There were ornaments of some kind at the gable's ends, but he couldn't tell what the figures were in the gloom. One had a still red-gleaming eye.

There was a door in front and one behind. He entered, brushing away the cobwebs, and was amazed to find himself inside a temple for the dead. He had heard talk about these, but mostly the Cusabo feared them and stayed away in order not to upset the spirits of those buried in the temples. Henry had not even been told where the temples were located. Now he walked in cautiously, but eager to see what was inside.

There were wooden slab coffins on benches and

smaller ones of woven cane. He looked around and then went to the rear entrance and glanced out. A shadowy figured melted into the undergrowth. He was startled, but to show that he meant no harm here he called out. Only the echo of his voice answered him in this woodland cavern.

Henry was uneasy. He might have broken a taboo by entering the temple at all. The Cusabo had never explained their burial ceremonies to him or made their feelings clear about the departed. Whoever it was he had seen might have been a guardian of the dead. On the other hand, he might have imagined that figure in such a dark, scary place. He didn't know, he really didn't. He had been around charnel houses before, but never had he experienced such a strange, unhappy feeling as here.

The doctor left the temple at once and got into his small dugout and paddled back to Orista. As he landed, he noticed at once that there were no Indians about. He walked up the beach into the town and was surprised to find it deserted. Though he called, no one answered; though he searched from hut to hut, he found each one empty.

45

Cooking fires were still burning, with pots of meat and vegetables simmering. Fish and strips of meat still broiled on their racks. The villagers had left suddenly. It was very strange. Had he violated a taboo by entering the temple? And had the shadowy figure come here and told the villagers that he was now unclean and they had best not come near him?

That was a possibility, but surely Pala would have stayed to tell him of his wrongdoing and help him. Surely?

Henry walked slowly through the village toward his hut. Suddenly he heard weird sounds coming from one of the dwellings. Cold sweat broke out on his brow. His neck bristled with fear. The sunset sky was streaked with blood red. Black shadows crept among the huts. What could it be that was here with him in this deserted village?

A Reluctant Farewell

Very cautiously Henry peered into the door. In the darkness something even darker was creeping toward him. He told himself that it was ridiculous to be frightened, that nothing from the spirit world could harm him, that no matter what it was he wouldn't run. Yet as the black shape crawled along the hut's floor toward him, he instinctively edged away.

Suddenly in the fading light a tiny Cusabo boy appeared, whimpering softly. With a cry of relief

Woodward sprang forward and snatched the naked child up.

"Hello, there, you bugaboo," he said aloud in English, hugging the boy to him. He was answered with coos of delight.

"Come," he said at last, glancing around the dark and deserted town. "We had best go to my dwelling and wait out the night."

Stew steamed over the fire by the hut, and Woodward gave the boy some broth. Then he ate and the two of them curled up together on the soft moss bed in a corner of the hut.

It was a moonlit night and the Englishman slept poorly. He was up often, wandering about his field and around the hut. Once he heard low, murmuring talk coming across the bay. Later there were sounds on the beach nearby, and he knew a landing had taken place. Who could this be? He had no idea, but he picked up his axe, his only weapon, and waited in the shadows.

Suddenly a voice called, "Heeen—reee!"

"Pala!" he yelled out in relief, feeling much the

fool for showing such un-British emotions. But he *was* glad she was back.

He shoved the pot of stew aside and built up the fire. Into its light came Pala, the chief, his wife, and several of the villagers.

"I am sorry we had to leave suddenly," the chief said. "But the Westo tribe has been raiding the country around here. Today we heard that their warriors were headed toward our town, so we left at once and went into the swamps." He looked about and sighed. "We Cusabos have never been great fighters," he went on. "We are a peace-loving people. The Westos are fierce. They have guns, while we have only bows. They enjoy battle; we do not. Worse than the Westos' destruction of our crops and towns is how they take away our children and women and eat them."

"Eat them!" exclaimed Henry. "The Westos are cannibals?"

The chief nodded. "All tribes are afraid of them, for they are powerful and control all the country to the west," he explained. "That is the reason the

Cusabos would like the English to settle near Orista. You can protect us, while we can help you in many ways in return."

Woodward agreed that it would be a fine situation for both.

"Also, the Guale Indians, who fight for the Spanish to the south of us, are pressing closer and closer to our territory," the chief said wearily. "We have troubles, many troubles."

There was a sudden loud wail from the hut and Woodward dashed inside for the child. He brought him out and handed him to the chief. "The boy and I held Orista safe from the invaders while you were away," he laughed.

"Ah," nodded the chief, "he was overlooked in our terrible haste to leave." Then he thanked Henry and he and his people went off to their dwellings.

The villagers settled back into their daily routine and Cusabo life continued as before. Woodward had much to ponder about the Westo Indians. After his countrymen settled here along the coast, they would push inland along the rivers where the land was fertile. Inland was the barrier of the Westos. It seemed these Indians would hardly welcome newcomers to their territory. It was something he would have to tell the Lords Proprietors. The Westos could be a hindrance to their settlements, much as the hostile Indians at Cape Fear had been. They could, in fact, be the cause of Carolina's failure.

However, that was not the only problem that Henry Woodward dwelt upon in the early summer of 1667. The other was the Spaniards of Florida and their Indian allies. Years ago Spanish priests had come to Orista and set up a wooden cross at the edge of the game field beside the town house; they had tried to convert the Indians.

Henry knew no villager paid the slightest heed to the Christian symbol. It was there as a tree might be there, and they passed it daily without a glance. But there were Spanish tools and utensils in the town. A few Spanish words were known and spoken; otherwise the nearest Spanish settlement, at St. Augustine, had left Orista alone.

England and Spain were not the best of friends

51

and had contested often over islands in the Caribbean. What of the future of Carolina? The Spanish would certainly pay strict attention to the new residents on their northern borders. But who could worry through the warm, lazy days? It was easier to play gambling games with his friends and dance and feast around the huge fires which brightened the nights on the game field. There was fishing with Pala, there was more exploring, and as always there were days to spend visiting and talking.

One morning the booming of a cannon sounded from the bay. Woodward thought it must be Sandford returning. He ran with the villagers to the beach. A Spanish ship floated there close to shore, its flag flapping from the mast.

Pala asked him if these newcomers were friends of his.

"No," he replied, "they are white men from another country. Spaniards. Probably from Florida, to the south of us."

"Oh," Pala said. "The men with the long robes who came and set up that thing of wood by the town house." Suddenly she turned to Henry and clutched his arm. "Perhaps it would be best if you hid. These people might be a danger to you."

"Hide from the Spaniards?" he snorted. "Nonsense! Carolina is a British province, and I am the legal tenant!"

Pala said nothing, but Henry could see she was uneasy.

A long boat filled with soldiers in armor and armed with swords and muskets left the ship and approached the shore. Their captain stood at the prow. His helmet glistened in the sun and a white plume waved from its crest. He called out in friendly fashion to the Indians. As the boat touched the shore, he leaped from it and greeted the chief respectfully. He glanced around at the crowd and his eyes came to rest on Henry Woodward.

He said something in Spanish and two soldiers rushed forward and seized the Englishman. Henry tried to jerk away, but he couldn't.

"What are you doing?" he shouted, his face flushed with rage. "This is not Spanish land! Let me go!"

None of the Spaniards understood him. He tried

the Cusabo language, but he was pushed toward the long boat, a Spanish prisoner.

There were cries of protest from the villagers. They edged toward the boat. The soldiers formed a ring around Woodward with their guns pointed at the Indians.

"Wait!" Henry cried to his friends. "There is nothing to be done. If you try to rescue me, you will be killed. Pala, run and fetch my black bag and clothes."

By the time he and the soldiers were settled in the boat, she was back. The captain snatched them from her and threw them in the boat and got in himself.

As they were rowed away, Woodward called back, "When they return, tell my friends where I have gone. And grieve not, I myself will return. Farewell for a while, my good Indian friends."

Pala and the other women began to wail and tear at their hair as they did when someone died. The chief stood with bowed head, ashamed that he could not stop this disgrace to his village. After all, he had pledged Woodward's safety to Colonel Sandford.

Henry shouted cheering words to him and to Pala, though he felt far from happy himself. What would happen to him now?

St Augustine and Back

There were four Spanish missions on the coast between Orista and St. Augustine, among the Guale Indians. This tribe was not on good terms with its neighbors. Therefore the boat stopped at each mission to make sure all went well with the priests and their wards. Several days passed before Woodward reached St. Augustine, where he was to be a prisoner, he was told.

St. Augustine was certainly a bustling port. Boats moved in and out of the docks in a steady

G.H. Simmons '76

stream—fishing boats, dugouts full of Indians, Spanish galleons with their accompanying pinnaces and sloops. Supply ships were unloading at the wharves. Boxes, bales, casks of wine, bags of fruit, and household furnishings were piled into waiting carts and sent rattling off.

The sandy streets of the town behind the waterfront were just as lively. Black slaves hastened along with buckets of shrimp and oysters and strings of fish over their shoulders. Spanish officers dashed to and fro on fine stallions, spurs jingling and saddles creaking. Dark-robed nuns and priests were everywhere. Indians stalked about in strange dress.

Life at Orista had been so slow-paced and easy-going. Here there was such flurry and haste and stirring about that Henry grew giddy watching.

The prisoner was marched to the wooden fort which guarded the harbor with its huge, menacing cannon. Here he was questioned by the commander, while a priest who spoke excellent English acted as interpreter. The officer wanted to know about British settlements in Carolina and future plans for colonization.

There was not much information Henry could give. Anyway, it was evident that the Spanish knew a great deal more about British endeavors on the American mainland than he did. Their ships plied the Carolina coast regularly, and little escaped their eyes. Time and again the commander pointed to a navigation chart lying on the table before Woodward; it was better than anything the Lords Proprietors had.

"We do not want you among the Cusabo Indians of Port Royal," the commander said finally. "We especially do not want the Indians to have among them a friend who might advise them to make war against the Guale Indians. Therefore we will hold you here for a while."

"I would not do such a thing," protested Henry.

The priest interrupted. "The Guale are peaceful Christians. Naturally the other tribes are looking for an excuse to raid them. It would be simple enough for you to encourage them.

"With the English settling Carolina, there will surely be trouble between us," the commander said. "Carolina is too close to Florida. We do not like such neighbors. You will be our hostage for a while."

The Tenant of all the Province of Carolina had come down in station in the New World. But things turned out better than Henry had dreamed they would. He was locked in his cell in the fort only at night. During the day he took his black doctor's bag and went with various priests, helping them on their visits to the sick in town and to the church plantations beyond. He was able to learn much useful information about military activity in Florida and about Catholic plans for Christianizing and controlling all the southern Indian tribes.

Late one night in 1668 the English pirate, Robert Searle, stormed St. Augustine. Houses and wharves were burned. Churches were looted of their silver and golden vessels. The soldiers and inhabitants were slaughtered mercilessly.

How Henry Woodward managed to get aboard Robert Searle's ship is unknown. But he did, and he sailed away, free of Spanish fetters. For a year he roved the West Indies with buccaneers, doctoring— perhaps barbering and bloodletting. Perhaps he took part in a raiding party, or other deeds he would never have dreamed of doing.

Always he was determined to get to England, to give the Lords Proprietors intelligence of the Indians and lands of Carolina, to tell them what he had learned among the Spanish in Florida. Whether the pirates considered him their captive and refused to let him leave is not known.

Yet it is known that in August 1669 Woodward was aboard a vessel bound for England. It was hurricane season, but most ship captains feared the buccaneers worse than hurricanes and considered their chances of safely leaving the West Indies better in stormy weather.

Woodward's ship had no trouble with pirates, but it was caught in a hurricane and wrecked on the coast of Nevis, one of the Leeward Islands of the West Indies. It seemed his plans to bring information to the Lords Proprietors were wrecked also—but not his ties to the Province of Carolina, for one of the three ships sent from England with new colonists and supplies for Carolina went astray and touched at Nevis also. Henry was only too happy to join the group as interpreter and Indian agent. And once more he was aboard a ship headed for Port Royal!

Carolina Colony

The ship, *Carolina,* left the West Indies and sailed for the coast of North America. Doctor Henry Woodward was coming back to the green wilderness of the New World. Though the ship made good time he was impatient to get back and begin what he hoped would be a life filled with riches and prestige. He would give up doctoring and take up trading with the many Indian tribes. He would acquire land and money and be a prominent man in Port Royal.

He was also eager to see Pala and the Orista

villagers once again. He wondered if they were still willing to help the British settle the area around Port Royal Bay. Surely they would not have changed their minds about that in the three years he had been gone.

The ship sailed too far north. When they landed they found they had missed Port Royal, and the Indians they met informed them that the Westo tribe had been raiding towns along the coast. Among these Indians was the chief of the Kiawah tribe. He stayed on board as the ship started south. This chieftain urged the English to settle near his town—just as, he pointed out, he had asked Sandford to settle there in 1666.

The Lords Proprietors, however, had wanted the colonists to settle at Port Royal because of the favorable reports they had gathered about the area. So William Sayle, who was to be the new governor of the Carolina settlement, ordered the ship to keep south.

As they approached the island where Orista was located, Henry grew quite excited. It might be that the town had been saved. But the sight which greeted

Woodward distressed him as few things ever had. Orista was destroyed. The houses were burned, and only portions of the town-house walls still stood. Pine seedlings had taken over the cornfields. A pile of rubble lay where once his own hut had stood.

For two days the ship rested there at anchor. During that time Henry and several of the Englishmen searched the countryside. One day they found a handful of Indians. They were Cusabo hiding from the Westo, but not the villagers of Orista.

When the Indians saw the white men, they came and rubbed their shoulders in their customary greeting. Then one said, *"Hiddy doddy Comorado Angles Westoe Skorrye."*

One of the Englishman turned to Woodward. "What did he say?"

"The English are very good friends but the Westos are naught," Henry replied.

Later, on board ship, a great argument began. Some wanted to land at once and begin to plant their gardens and fields. Others said this place was too exposed to the Spanish and the Guale Indians. The

chief of Kiawah said the Guale Indians were only a short distance away. He urged the Englishmen to come to his region, where there were a great many towns and a great many bowmen to act as allies.

Some of the passengers wanted to follow this suggestion, even if it meant a few more days aboard the crowded vessel. As Nicholas Carteret, one of the colonists from England, later wrote, the chief was "a very ingenius Indian and a great linguist in this maine." But Governor Sayle wanted to leave this deserted area and settled at Kiawah. Most of those aboard finally agreed to follow him there, Henry Woodward among them.

So the *Carolina* sailed away, and Henry bid the ruins of Orista a silent farewell. He doubted that he would ever again see Pala or any of the villagers. However, he couldn't stay sad long when he thought of the new Indian villages he would visit soon and the new Indian friends he would make.

The colonists settled at Albemarle Point, on a river they named the Ashley for one of the Lords Proprietors. Within a few months Spanish war vessels blocked the river's mouth, together with a fleet of dugouts filled with Guale Indians. They prepared to land and attack Albemarle Point.

A summons for help went out to the scattered Indian towns. By the time the Carolinians were ready to fight, the Kiawah and their allies had arrived. Meanwhile a storm had blown the Spanish boats out to sea, leaving only the Guale Indians to attack the English. But seeing so many Kiawah bowmen advance on them, they quickly paddled away. The new settlement was saved because the chief of Kiawah helped the newcomers as he had promised. How glad they were now that they had settled where Indians stood ready to fight beside them.

Henry Woodward hoped the mutual friendship would continue. He knew that the fate of the young colony might well depend on the Kiawah Indians for protection, and for food as well. In a large part it would also depend on him as interpreter whether white and red men got along happily together. For a while at least, his fate and that of the new colony were in his own hands.

Back to the Wilderness

Through the early years of the colony Woodward's part can only be guessed, from various brief mentions of him in letters to England. One settler wrote that he was "the only person by whose meanes wee hold a faire and peasable correspondence with the natives of the Place . . ."

It is known that he made frequent journeys inland to visit various tribes, making allies for the Kiawahs and the British. He made one journey by land to Virginia which upset the new South Carolina governor, Joseph West. West complained to Lord

Ashley that Woodward's absence inconvenienced the settlers in communicating with their red neighbors.

On another expedition to the interior, Woodward made friends with the chieftain of Cofitachiqui, expecting to open a trade with that distant nation. But this never came about because of the hostility of the Westos.

The Westos! The feared savage fighters, with their cruel ways and cannibal customs! They were holding back the infant colony's efforts to get skins and furs, robbing the British of a chance for much-needed business profits. As Woodward had understood long ago in Orista, something would have to be done some day about the Westos. But what? And how?

Then in 1674 Lord Ashley made Henry Woodward his agent to trade from his plantation, St. Giles, with neighboring Indians. Ashley instructed Woodward to determine whether it would be better to make peace with a distant tribe called the Cussitaws, who might be persuaded to destroy the Westo; or whether it would help trade to try to make peace and be on friendly terms with the Westos.

"Easy enough to give such orders when you are writing from England," Henry complained to one of his Kiawah guides. "Here in Carolina I don't see how I can arrange to be friends with either one. Do you?"

The Kiawah agreed it was a difficult problem, and he could offer no suggestions as to how to go about solving it.

In the fall of 1674, those at St. Giles were startled by the sudden appearance of ten Westo Indians demanding to trade. Woodward was in Charles Town, but he was sent for at once. He hastened up the Ashley River in a yawl and found the waiting Indians finished with their trading. He invited them to stay at St. Giles for the night. No. They were leaving at once. They indicated by signs and a few Kiawah words that they wanted someone to go to their towns to discuss trade activities with their chieftain. Henry knew it had to be him. No one else dared risk going.

"Do not go," begged his Kiawah guide. "The Westos will chop you to pieces and boil your flesh and bones for stew."

Perhaps the Westos knew Woodward had visited the towns of their enemies on missions. They might be lying about wanting trade. And they were not known to keep their word about anything. They were tricky. In recent years they had killed white men close to the settlements. Would they kill him also?

Yet here was the opportunity he had been wanting for so long—a chance to go into the Westo Nation and open trade and agree on peace terms. Were they sincere in their request?

He stood there debating with himself, weighing the bad with the good. The leader tapped Henry on the shoulder and beckoned him to come with them. He pointed toward the woods.

Henry nodded. He would go! He might never have such an opportunity as this again. His employer, Lord Ashley, would appreciate the risks he was taking. Perhaps he might give Woodward a greater percentage of the profits if this trading venture were successful.

Turning to his Kiawah guide, he said, "Go with me and I will see that you get a new musket and bags and bags of trade beads."

The guide shook his head. "I would not go among the Westo for anything you offered me," he replied. "I enjoy life too much to throw it away so recklessly."

Woodward shrugged and began his preparations to leave. He put on a deerskin shirt, coarse woolen breeches, Indian moccasins and, of course, his floppy black hat. He carried some food, his weapons and a blanket. The ten Westos trotted off and Henry fell into line with them. It was October 10, 1674, a Saturday afternoon with the weather raw and a cold drizzle falling. At the edge of a field Woodward glanced back at the windows of St. Giles, alight in the fall gloom. Would he see the plantation and trading post again?

He turned and disappeared with his companions into the trees.

Perils in the Rain

The afternoon continued wet and in a short time his clothes were soaked. The Westos didn't mind the rain. Most of them wore only breechclouts and moccasins and the water flowed off their greased bodies unnoticed. All of the party seemed only concerned about keeping dry the things for which they had traded their skins at St. Giles.

The Indians ignored Woodward. They didn't slow their pace for him. He was not bothered by this, for he was used to their jogging gait from his frequent travels with other Indians. It was the best way to cover great distances through the woods without too much exertion.

However, he was a little uneasy that these ten weren't more friendly, for he didn't know what this might mean. Once he fell from a log as they crossed a stream. He came up out of the water spluttering and found that the Indians had jogged on.

Woodward wanted no offer of a hand up the slippery bank. He had been out in the wilderness long enough to know how to help himself. But how different the Westos were compared to the courteous Cusabos and Kiawahs and the other coastal Indians. They would have been concerned about his safety.

Night came early among the trees. They stopped, and two huts covered with bark were quickly erected. These didn't entirely keep out the rain, but they were better than nothing. A fire was built in each. Without being told to, Woodward went into the first one finished. The leader and four warriors filed in after him.

The leader was shorter and heavier than the

others. He made no gesture of friendship to Woodward, nor did he try to talk to him. Henry kept silent also. But he noticed that whatever move he made, the leader's cold black eyes were on him.

At first Henry didn't mind. But as the night passed, this constant surveillance made him uneasy. What did it mean? Was the Indian just curious about whites? Or was he waiting till Woodward went to sleep to sink a tomahawk into his brain? The other Westos had gone to sleep at once. Henry didn't care for the way the leader fingered his wool blanket, or the way his eyes stared at Henry's weapons time and again. Was he going to murder him for his possessions?

He kept busy and awake by drying his moccasins thoroughly. Indian shoes were the only footwear for forest travel, but they certainly didn't keep out the wet. The leather was now stiff, so he worked it about in his hands till the shoes were soft enough to slip on. After tying the long leather thongs about his ankles, he dried his blanket.

The leader followed his every move. Once Henry

stared straight back at him, hoping he would cease this watchfulness. The Westo's eyes did not turn. It was Woodward who finally had to look away.

He yawned several times. He was wearier than he had thought. He wouldn't be able to keep his eyes open much longer. Henry glanced at the Westo leader, who was wide awake and still watching him. Henry stood at the fire and dried his blanket a while longer. At last he decided he'd have to have some sleep, no matter the chance he took.

Sitting down beside his pack and weapons with the warm blanket wrapped around him, he rested his head on his upraised knees. He would be more alert dozing this way than lying down.

The fire had burned low when Henry awoke. Groggily he raised his head and found himself staring into the barrel of his own pistol. The Westo leader squatted beside him, inspecting the weapon. The cock was back in firing position, the Indian's finger on the trigger.

Henry was so startled he could neither move nor speak. The Westo pulled the trigger.

Journey's End

The flint in the cock sprang forward against the powder pan cover and knocked it open. But there was no flash and no bullet fired. The powder was too wet for the flint sparks to ignite.

A sigh of relief flooded through Woodward. Had the Westo meant to kill him? Or had he never seen a pistol before and had the firing of it been an accident? Either way, Henry had come close to being a dead Carolinian.

The Westo placed the pistol back beside the gun

and lay down near his sleeping companions beside the fire. Henry got up and walked stiffly to the blaze, threw on more branches and wood, and this time stretched out to sleep. But it was near daylight before he was able to close his eyes.

The following day rain still fell, but they were off early, sloshing through the puddles and mud. The leader ran right at Henry's heels. The pistol hadn't worked—was the Westo now going to wait and strike the white man down with his tomahawk whenever it pleased him to do so, Henry wondered tensely?

Still he could do little about the situation but put thoughts of murder from his mind. He would have to believe the Westo tribe wanted trade with the English, that they wanted him alive. So he concentrated on keeping pace. Never had he run for such a long period each day, and day after day with so little rest. Yet he was certainly not going to ask them to slow down for him.

Through hardwood forests they jogged, onward through pine woods where the air was sweet with the smell of resin, across savannahs of tall grass turned golden by the autumn cold. Northwest at first, then westward, steadily westward they headed. Woodward could only guess that their destination was the big stream called the Westo by Carolina Indians, but by the British called the May River.

Food was plentiful and easily obtained. A turkey, startled up out of the bushes by their passage, was quickly brought down with an arrow and ended on a roasting spit that night. A deer, drinking at a stream and aware of them too late to run, received several arrows. Warm turkey breast, deer collops and parched corn flour broth were very satisfying after a hard day's run, Henry found. The Westos urged him to eat heartily, though they never took their eyes from him as he chewed his food.

Henry admired the skill of these Indians with bow and arrow. They could get off several arrows before a man could possibly fire his gun once, he saw. What warriors!

"Now," he told himself, "if they become as adept with the guns I want to trade to them, heaven help the other Indians. No tribe would be able to stand up to them in warfare."

It was pleasant to contemplate. As allies of the English, the Westo could protect Carolina along its western and northern frontiers, and he and Lord Ashley could make a great deal of money from trading the guns. Suddenly all the chances he had taken to make this journey seemed worthwhile.

"All I have to do," he thought, "is make the chieftain of the whole tribe trust and like me."

Saturday they arrived at the banks of the Westo River and crossed to a small town, where the chief entertained Woodward with a feast while the travelers waited for the rain to stop. Not a word was spoken to him. Occasionally the chief gestured politely that the white man should eat. Once again he was the object of everyone's stares.

When the weather cleared, he got into a dugout and was paddled upstream toward the principal town where the great leader of the Westo lived. Henry began to clean his weapons, scraping the caked powder from the pans of both guns. Then he loaded them with dry powder. It was proper when approaching an Indian town to fire your guns and let all know you had arrived.

Suddenly, rounding a bend, before him on a cliff stood the high picket walls of a fortified town. It looked quite formidable and Henry was impressed. No enemy Indians would be able to take this town by assault.

He fired first his fusil, then his pistol. A volley of gunfire answered from the town. Then the huge wooden gate swung open. The paddlers guided the boat in among hundreds of other dugouts. Never had Woodward seen so many dugouts. It must be a larger town than he had imagined to have such a number of boats.

He jumped out and began climbing up the steep cliffside. A large town filled with a multitude of Indians—and its trade was his, if all went well with this meeting. If not, his life might be in jeopardy. He took a deep breath and pushed upward, with his heart pounding wildly.

The Westo Land

Two lines of warriors waited at the gate. Their headdresses were very colorful, some with dyed deer tails and bright feathers, others with sparkling bangles. Bracelets dangled about their wrists and tortoiseshell rattles hung from their legs. Around their necks they wore strings of bear teeth, colored stones and pearls.

The warriors were quite impressive, but Henry was more interested in the guns which they raised in salute to him. He could see they were not of Spanish

85

make, and that pleased him. He wanted the Westo trade to belong to him and Ashley alone. Since the weapons were British, he supposed they had traveled northward to Virginia to trade. That could easily be stopped if his mission today succeeded.

With Woodward in their midst the Westo marched off through the town. It was a great honor to be welcomed in this fashion, with a ceremony such as any important white or Indian leader would receive. He knew there was no friendliness connected with it. It didn't mean all was well with his visit. He still had to prove to them that he was their friend and would trust them in all their dealings and enterprises.

As they passed through the streets, Henry noticed on top of each dwelling a pole from which dried and painted scalps hung. Some of them appeared to have been taken only a few days before. He shuddered. Scalps were not a pleasant thing to think about ever—and especially not here and now.

Nor should he let his eyes search each pile of refuse they passed for signs of human bones. If the Westos were cannibals, he would know about it soon enough. He tried hard to put such thoughts from his head and to conceal his nervousness from the Indians.

The Indians pressed around the procession, hundreds of men, women and children. There was no shouting, no laughter or cry of welcome. The Westo were only interested in getting a glimpse of him. Was he the first white man they had ever seen? Or was he the first to enter their town? It might be so. He threw back his head and stepped along with as lordly an air as he could summon, though his heart pounded loudly in his chest.

The chieftain met Henry at the door of his dwelling and led the way inside, indicating a stool where Woodward was to sit. The Westo leader sat on another stool, facing him across a low-burning fire. The warrior escort filed into the house and stood around the two seated figures. Then the villagers began to crowd inside.

Henry glanced around. He was the center of attention, yet no one looked at him with friendliness or kindliness. All the faces were as stiff and unsmiling as carved masks. No other tribe Henry had lived among in the past few years had been so reserved. This was a solemn occasion, but surely not quite this serious.

The chief watched him with eyes that were bright and alive but told Henry nothing. All waited while the last of the villagers squeezed inside.

Suddenly there was a scrambling across the bark covering overhead. Bits of wood and dust fell on Woodward. He glanced up to see the roof torn apart and the tiny face of a little boy peering down at him. Henry smiled and waved and then stopped, wondering if he had done the wrong thing.

The boy smiled back and began to widen the hole. In reaching out to remove a slab of bark he lost his balance and came hurtling down with a cry of terror.

Henry leaped from his stool and dashed forward, stumbling over the fire-tender. He almost fell but managed to keep his balance and be under the boy with open arms. He caught him easily, for he was light as down.

"Is the sight of me worth a busted head?" he

asked the boy aloud, holding him up before him. The boy caught his breath and reached and touched Henry's nose.

There was a hubbub in the dwelling, cries and cheers and what sounded like a happy chant. The chief stood beside Henry, a wide grin on his face. He held out his arms for the boy, but the child grabbed Henry around the neck and wouldn't let go.

Woodward motioned that it was all right and took his seat on the stool with the boy in his lap. The chieftain began to speak and he went on and on for the rest of the afternoon. The boy went to sleep and Henry wished he could join him. It had been a tiring week traveling here, and today's pressure had added to his exhaustion. But thanks to his little sleeping Westo friend, all was well. He had no doubts about that now. A glance around at the beaming faces and the gestures of the chief as he spoke assured Henry that the Westos were his friends and the trade was his.

A Carolinian
and an American

Woodward stayed among the Westos ten days, feasting with them and roaming about the country-side in their company. He discovered that they didn't eat human flesh. Other tribes had spread the idea through hatred of them.

By November 6 he was home again at St. Giles. He took his time, however, about writing his employer in England of his success. It was not until December 31 that he set down for Lord Ashley a faithful account of his Westo journey. He ended that letter by saying he expected the Westos back the following March with deerskins, furs and young Indian slaves. Woodward knew well the possibilities which lay in those three items. All Indian tribes could obtain them, and they were always anxious to trade them for the white man's goods, thus leaving behind their former stone-age life. Henry's hazardous journey had helped to begin the wealth and expansion of the colony of South Carolina. Securing the Westo trade had also laid the cornerstone of the colony's Indian system, which was to affect its history throughout the colonial period.

The British surgeon's example, taking chances to go to distant Indian tribes for trade and alliances, was followed by later bold Carolinians. These traders pushed steadily inland until, only three decades after the founding of Charles Town in 1670, they were at the Mississippi River, competing with France for the loyalty of the red tribes in America's heartland. It is a remarkable story. Yet who would have thought it would begin with a young man's wish to live among the Cusabo, at Port Royal in 1666? Certainly not Henry Woodward.

Of Woodward's life after his Westo venture there are a few scattered references over the years. In 1677 he was made deputy for Lord Ashley's many Carolina enterprises. This was a position he certainly had earned by the chances he had taken in the uncharted regions of Carolina, and the dangers involved in the many expeditions he undertook for his patron.

Within three years, however, he was in disgrace in the colony. There were accusations that Woodward had incited his friends, the Westos, to raid the peaceful Cusabos—once also his friends. His trading activities were forbidden and he was fined. The Carolinians then went to war against the Westos and most of the tribe were killed or driven from the colony.

Henry Woodward had never been one to take misfortune without a struggle. Now his good name and his future life in Carolina were at stake. He sailed for England and laid his case before Lord Ashley and the other Carolina Proprietors. Here was an Indian agent who had been invaluable to them. And it seemed that the accusations against him had been made by men jealous of Woodward's influence with the Westos and other Indians. Such rivalry would never do in the infant colony. Woodward was pardoned and the money he had paid as a fine was returned. Once again he had survived.

It was a short time thereafter that Lord Ashley lost his influence and power in England, and thus in Carolina. Woodward was in trouble again with the loss of his good patron, for he was no longer the colony's greatest Indian agent. Nevertheless, he now had a wife and two sons to support. The occupation of surgeon he had dropped long ago; trading with the Indians was what he knew and could do best. He kept on, apparently working on his own. How much trading he did is not clear by the records, but a venture of his to the Lower Creek Indians in 1686 is recorded. From this expedition it was reported he returned dangerously ill, carried in a litter by the red men. With him were 150 Indian beavers, laden with pelts.

Henry may not have recovered from this enterprise. Perhaps he died shortly after, or perhaps he lingered for a few years. Historians place his death sometime before 1690, when he was in his early forties.

But, surely in his fading days he recalled with pleasure the beauties of the southern wilderness through which he had traveled. Surely he remembered and mulled over his many friendships with far-flung Indian tribes. Surely his accomplishments in this raw green world of America made him proud and eased his pain somewhat. The unknown regions had not swallowed him up without a trace, nor had they defeated him. Here he had proven his courage and his worth. He was a Carolinian and an American. Honors were his.

THE END